SCOTTISH BEASTIES®

POCKET FIELD GUIDE

Lachie Dundurn

Airo Limited

Airo Limited

ISBN 978-0-9566486-0-0

Published by Airo Limited
© Airo Limited 2010

SCOTTISH BEASTIES

is a Registered Trade Mark used under licence by Airo Limited.

www.airoltd.co.uk

A CIP catalogue record for this book is available from the British Library

Printed in Scotland

CONTENTS

SCOTTISH BEASTIES

To whom it may concern,

I, Lachlan Murdo Dundurn, being of sound mind and able body, do hereby anticipate my disappearance off the face of this earth.

If you are reading this letter, then my prediction will have come true.

To that end, I should be obliged if you would advise the Authorities to desist in their searches. They will have found no trace of me nor will they ever, as I have been taken underground by the Faeries.

I appreciate that you dear reader, living in the modern world, will believe this statement to be the ramblings of a confused old hermit. However, after examining the contents of my trunk, I am confident that there will be sufficient evidence therein to persuade you otherwise.

Never forget, there are many things that we humans do not understand about the Natural World. The further we move away from Nature and into our urban lives, the greater our ignorance of the beasties in remote locations becomes. So I beseech you, please retain an open mind.

Within the chest, noted and illustrated to the best of my abilities, lie the results of over 50 years of observations and interactions with a hidden world. Until my safe return, I bequeath you the trusteeship of this information.

Use this knowledge wisely and if you are able, share it with others to engender a greater understanding of the wonders that lie around us waiting to be discovered.

I look forward to meeting with you some day when I have made good my escape from the Wee Folk.

Yours aye,
Lachie M. Dundurn.

Lachie disappeared from his croft in the remote North West of Scotland sometime between April and May of 2010.

Having no family and few friends, the above letter (containing a key) and one locked trunk were deposited anonymously at my office door. The contents of the chest are amazing and, when time allows me, more will be revealed.

However, initially and in accordance with Lachie's wishes, I have published this Guide to help people benefit from his field craft expertise.

An artist was used to tidy up the sketches but to give a flavour of Lachie's original manuscripts, unedited excerpts from his numerous observations have been included in the 'Notes' section.

The Midgie and the Fly gain inclusion in this Compendium not for their rarity but as a warning to other would-be trackers. They infuriated and tormented Lachie continuously unlike the Golden Eagle which was a favourite.

I hope that you find this Field Guide to be enlightening and wish you many happy hours of tracking.

The Editor,
Airo Limited (Publishing House).

Lachie Dundurn has spent his life tracking creatures.

He understands that we follow in the footsteps of our hunter gatherer ancestors from thousands of years ago. This connection with the past appeals greatly to him and adds to the sense of expectation he feels every time he goes on a beastie hunt.

Taken from his journal, this is Lachie's advice on how to get the most from your field trip:

1   Ensure that your clothing blends in with your surroundings and that you wear appropriate footwear.

2   Pack food, drink, a warm rug and some waterproofs as these will help you stay comfortable when on a stake out.

3   A monocular brings you closer to your quarry (unlike Lachie, you may prefer to use a pair of binoculars).

4   Always carry a notebook and pencil to record your observations.

5   Be aware of the tell tale signs that are around you e.g. paw prints; fur left on bushes; gnawed, discarded food and animal droppings.

6   Listen out for beastie 'call' signs.

7   Move as slowly and as quietly as you can.

8   Stay downwind in case the beasties smell you.

9   Be patient.

10   Enjoy yourself.

On the following pages, a series of symbols are used to highlight characteristics of the relevant beastie profiled.

Explanations of these symbols are as follows:

 Diurnal - awake during the day, sleeps during the night.

 Nocturnal - awake during the night, sleeps during the day.

 Hibernates - goes into a deep sleep during the winter months.

 Does not hibernate - same activity levels throughout the year.

 Solitary existence - lives alone for most of its life.

 Pack existence - lives in a group for most of its life.

 Prey - other beasties want to eat it.

 Predator - it wants to eat other beasties.

Please note that it is possible for a beastie to have two symbols that appear to contradict each other. For example, if we featured a spider (we don't) it would be shown as both predator and prey as it hunts insects yet is hunted by birds, bats, shrews etc.

7

An adult Bampot out for a stroll.

The Bampot's skin looks and sounds like metal but is in fact a very hard, leathery texture. Humans have hunted them as a source of cookware for centuries though this practice ended with the introduction of man-made pots and pans. An adult stands at around 90cm in height and weighs up to 20kg.

They live in clachans (small villages) where the oldest Bampot is chieftain. Every house is built to highlight the owner's hobby, making for some truly bizarre looking homes. This only adds to the impression that it is the lunatics who are running the asylum when you enter a Bampot village!

Interesting Facts

- Bampots cherish 'Full Moons', so spend most of each month trying to repair them.
- Collective name - a 'loon.'
- Breeding season - all year round.
- Potential as a human pet - yes, many a family has a Bampot in it.
- Bampots will eat anything if told it is food.

Where found in Scotland

8

Tracking Tips

- Unaware of the art of camouflage, Bampots are relatively easy to track.
- Identification 'call' - a repeated mumbling noise that sounds like 'Eh?'
- Defensive strategies - no universal behaviour for this species.
- Natural habitat - remote, deserted glens.
- Behavioural habits - expect the unexpected.

A baby Bampot.

Bampots give birth to up to five live young known as 'Bams'. They have wrinkle-free arms, legs and necks. Appropriately, they love their 'dummies' (bath plugs) and wear shorts with a slit up the back for 'potty' training. Bams suffer from 'potty botty' (crusty, rusty bottom rash).

The Bampot paw print is similar to a pan lid.

TRACKING

EASY ⟷ HARD

9

The adult Bluebottle

The Bluebottle is the yobbish football hooligan of the insect world. Loud, stupid and annoying, they love being in the middle of pooh! They are very common and delight in this fact. They are scavengers who love eating dead bodies, rotting vegetation, manure or sucking on the leaky bits around scabs of wounded animals.

A Bluebottle grows up to a length of 14mm and weighs 15mg. They will sleep anywhere that is sheltered from the wind and the rain. With no social hierarchy a Fly swarm is complete bedlam.

Interesting Facts

- A Fly's eye contains over 4,000 lenses yet they have poor sight.
- Collective name - a 'swarm.'
- Breeding season - most active in the summer months.
- Potential as a human pet - definitely not.
- 30,000 Flies per week can hatch from one rubbish bin.
- Flies vomit on their food to help dissolve it.
- Flies pooh when they eat - nice table manners!

Where found in Scotland

10

Tracking Tips

A baby Bluebottle (Maggot).

- Bluebottles are easy to track - they find you. It's getting rid of them that's the problem!

- Identification 'call' - a loud buzz.

- Defensive strategies - they flee but then forget the danger and come back again.

- Natural habitat - widespread throughout Scotland.

- Behavioural habits - most fond of flying around, bumping into things and looking for something 'good' to eat.

How would you feel if your Mum left you to fend for yourself on a piece of rotting meat or pile of pooh? Well, Maggots love it! The female can lay up to 500 eggs in clusters of 20 or more. The eggs hatch into Larvae (also known as Maggots).

Before the Romans altered the calendar, the month of July used to be known as 'Worm' month due to the large amount of Maggots (Worms) found on stored human food.

Right: Tiny 'Bother Boot' tracks (note the 'BB' in the heel erroneously believed to stand for 'Bluebottle').

TRACKING

EASY ⟵⟶ HARD

11

An adult Bogle.

The Bogle, being of a spectral nature, is hard to see but very easy to sense. The atmosphere positively crackles with tension when one is nearby and all animal and bird noises fade into an eerie silence.

Interesting Facts

- Collective name - a 'blast'.
- Breeding Season - one night per year - Halloween.
- Potential as a human pet - definitely not. It would be a living nightmare (literally) to have one anywhere near you.
- Bogles can kill humans with a single touch, though they rarely do.

The Bogle is one of the 'living' dead so it does not need to eat or drink. They are solitary creatures so there is no such thing as a social hierarchy. As it is ethereal, it can stretch to any height whilst its weight remains lighter than air. They can make their abodes anywhere they wish from human houses to hillside caves.

Where found in Scotland

12

Tracking Tips

A young Bogle (Whiff).

- Being virtually invisible, Bogles are very hard to track.
- Identification 'call' - an unearthly low pitched moaning accompanied by an intensely cold gust of wind.
- Defensive strategies - they have been known to flee but usually it is the Bogle that does the challenging.
- Natural habitat - it is capable of 'living' anywhere it chooses.
- Behavioural habits - best known for being a nuisance to living creatures (by scaring them or disrupting their labours), Bogles are capable of turning deadly if angered.

Bogles give birth to 'live' young called 'Whiffs'. The size of litter is always one as it takes decades for a youngster to reach maturity. Most humans are unaware that Whiffs even exist but tell tale signs of one being nearby are when people say things like 'Brrr! That's a nasty little draught' or 'Oooh! I feel as if someone has just walked over my grave!'

Right: A trail winding through grass or crops, leading nowhere and which invariably stops abruptly. If the tracks are fresh, there will be wisps of odourless 'smoke' hanging in the air on either side of the path.

TRACKING

EASY ←——————→ HARD

13

An adult Cloud.

Clouds enjoy hanging around in groups. They try and hide their true forms as humans don't believe that Clouds are alive. However, if you look long enough, you will spot different shapes forming when they don't think people are looking.

Interesting Facts

- Collective name - a 'bank.'
- Breeding Season - all year round.
- Potential as human pet - not dangerous but not practical either.
- Clouds are classified into 10 different types dependent upon their height and appearance.
- Clouds on Earth are made of water or ice whereas on Saturn they are composed of liquid methane.

Adult Clouds vary in size but can grow to vast proportions whilst remaining as light as feathers.

Their nests float throughout the sky and increase in size as the Wisp grows. Clouds gain sustenance from moisture soaked up when passing over sources of water like lochs, wetlands and seas so they are classed as neither prey nor predators.

Clouds have no social structure but the bigger the beastie, the more they can throw their weightlessness around to dominate a particular patch of sky. Occasionally, these territorial claims can result in thunderstorms when big Clouds clash with each other.

Where found in Scotland

A young Cloud.

Tracking Tips

- Clouds are easy to track. Go outside, look skywards and anything that looks like cotton wool is likely to be a Cloud!
- Identification 'call' - Clouds can talk in any human 'tongue' but they are best known for their own language - thunder.
- Defensive strategies - they have no predators so no defensive strategies are required.
- Natural habitat - anywhere in the sky.
- Behavioural habits - Clouds can be dark and moody or light and carefree. They are Mother Nature's drifters who love observing life on Earth below them.

Clouds give birth to one 'live' baby known as a 'Wisp'. Wisps are notoriously hard to potty train. Indeed many a Cloud never learns proper bladder control and suffers from the embarrassing problem of 'head wetting' right through their adult lives.

Right: Look for raindrops or puddles on the ground dependent upon the size of Cloud you are tracking.

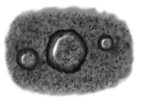

TRACKING

EASY ←——————→ HARD

15

An adult Domesticated Haggis.

At a casual glance, Domesticated Haggis are similar to piglets but they are easily distinguishable from their porcine neighbours by the distinctive snouts unique to all Haggis breeds. Unlike their horns, this physical characteristic is not being lost in the intensive breeding programme created to rear these creatures as a Scottish culinary delicacy.

Domesticated Haggis nest in cosy 'Mother and Hog' barns whilst the adult males are free to forage in securely enclosed fields. They consume most foodstuffs with relish having a diet similar to that of pigs. They grow to a height of 60cm (to the shoulder) and weigh up to 25kg.

As far as social hierarchy goes, the Domesticated Haggis, being a bred animal, considers the farmer and his dogs as the chieftain and elders of their 'thicket'.

Interesting Facts

- Collective name - a 'thicket'.
- Breeding Season - in the Springtime for fattening up by January the 25th of the following year.
- Potential as a human pet - excellent. They are loyal, loving and trusting.
- Domesticated Haggis are one of the few animals which puts on weight in the early part of Winter.

Where found in Scotland

Tracking Tips

A young Haggis (Hog).

Domesticated Haggis have litters of between six and eight 'live' young known as 'Hogs'. These young are highly prized by Haggis farmers who ensure that their every need is catered for. From an early age, these pampered creatures are taught to concentrate on getting really plump and juicy…and they comply with this regime eagerly.

Right: Note the evolutionary transition to the cloven hoof from the paw print. Compare this track to that of their wild cousins, the Hairy Horny Haggis.

- Domesticated Haggis don't need tracked - just visit them on the Haggis farms.
- Identification 'call' - a 'honk' (similar to the Hairy Horny Haggis but with a higher pitch).
- Defensive strategies - none. They wag their tails at everyone.
- Natural habitat - farm fields and barns.
- Behavioural habits - they have a simple enthusiasm for everything especially Burns' Night where they have been told that they are the guests of honour.

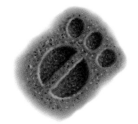

TRACKING

EASY ←——————→ HARD

17

A Faerie

Faeries are notoriously difficult to observe as they will be tracking you long before you see any signs of them. To have any chance, you must be staked out in a well-concealed hide long before sundown. If discovered, be prepared to be on the end of some extreme pranks!

Interesting Facts

- Collective name - a 'rammy.'
- Breeding Season - each Equinox and Solstice.
- Potential as human pet - definitely not! The 'owners' would be made to pay dearly for even attempting it.
- Faeries turn to stone if just one ray of sunshine hits their bodies (possible origins of the garden gnome?).

Faeries share the same diet as humans but only grow to a height of 120cm and weigh 30 kgs. They live a subterranean life during daylight hours often in sumptuous palaces that have taken many generations to complete. These palaces are filled with priceless treasures and artefacts collected, stolen or tricked from other species down through the centuries. Their social hierarchy is one of dictatorship. Faeries admire a strong (and cruel) leader if he brings in the 'rewards' and are quite happy to tolerate summary justice if this is the case. However, if the king fails to lead them to success, then he is assured of a 'sticky' end!

Where found in Scotland

A young Faerie (Faertie)

Tracking Tips

- Faeries, being the masters of camouflage, are extremely difficult to track.
- Identification 'call' - they can mimic all animal sounds so it is impossible to distinguish theirs from a real creature's cry.
- Defensive strategies - camouflage, stealth attack or flee depending upon what has threatened them…but rest assured, they will always get their revenge!
- Natural habitat - usually underground but anywhere away from direct sunlight could be used e.g. woodland dells.
- Behavioural habits - when they aren't mischief-making, they are masters at cheating on a deal.

The young of a Faerie is called a 'Faertie' and it is very unusual for there to be more than two born per litter. Faerties are cowardly (possibly the origin of the Scots' word 'Feartie') but naughty from an early age. Skewering their favourite teddy and electrocuting their baby sitter with the Faerie lights cord is actively encouraged by their parents as good practice for adult life.

Right: Note the extreme narrowness of the boot print, tapering to a fine point at the tip.

TRACKING

EASY ⟵⟶ HARD

An adult Golden Eagle

These magnificent birds of prey lead solitary lives hence have little need of a social hierarchy outside the family group of two adults and Eaglets. They hunt grouse, hare and ptarmigan and scavenge on any carrion found on the mountainsides. They have a wingspan of up to 240cm and weigh in excess of 7kgs.

Golden Eagles choose to live in remote locations. They are sensitive to human contact and will fly away if disturbed. This can be a problem in February and March when they are incubating eggs. The Eagle's eyrie is a massive structure of sticks and heather which is insulated with grass and bracken. These nests are sited upon cliffs or crags up to 2,000 feet above sea level.

Interesting Facts

- An Eagle's nest is called an eyrie.
- Collective name - a 'convocation'.
- Breeding season - in the Spring.
- Potential as a human pet - possible, but don't give it a cuddle!
- They will hunt in pairs during the lean winter months.

Where found in Scotland

20

A young Eagle (Eaglet)

Tracking Tips

- Due to their size, Golden Eagles are relatively easy to track.
- Identification 'call' - a high pitched 'yelp' though rarely used.
- Defensive strategies - flee if disturbed by either humans or 'mobbed' by other smaller birds.
- Natural habitat - open tree-less moors and mountainous areas.
- Behavioural habits - an Eagle performing a 'display' flight to a mate is a joy to see.

Eagles lay up to four eggs in one brood though only one survives usually. The young are called 'Eaglets' and whilst they may look cute, these chicks will steal the food from their siblings' mouths to ensure their own survival. However, despite this trait, they are known to be very polite to guests and prey alike…before eating them!

If you are lucky enough to find a track in the mud, note the sheer size of the print and the depth of the talon marks.

TRACKING

EASY ⟵⟶ HARD

21

A Hairy Horny Haggis

Hairy Horny Haggis grow to a height of 75cm, weigh about 18kgs and yearn for the quiet life. Each clan is led by a chieftain and a group of elders.

Interesting Facts

• Humans believe that the Hairy Horny Haggis has been extinct for centuries whereas it thrives unseen in places like Glen Wheesht.

• Collective name - a 'clan'.

• Breeding season - all year.

• Potential as a human pet - possible …if people knew they existed.

• They are vegetarians and excellent organic farmers.

As Scotland's rarest beasties, Hairy Horny Haggis are difficult to track. Their predators include Golden Eagles and humans which explains why the Haggis choose to live in the Caledonian Forest. The tree branches shelter them from aerial attack and the undergrowth provides plenty of hiding places.

Their underground nests are called 'hamelldaemes'. These are shaped like quaichs (the traditional Scottish drinking cups of friendship) and are built on three levels to slow down humans in a 'digging out' attack.

Where found in Scotland

A young Haggis (Hog)

Tracking Tips

- The tracker must find the home territory of the Hairy Horny Haggis to have any chance of observing these elusive beasties.
- Identification 'call' - a delicate 'honk' though generally the Haggis prefer to talk.
- Defensive strategies - camouflage or flee.
- Natural habitat - the Great Wood of Caledon.
- Behavioural habits - they enjoy the peaceful life and try to avoid confrontation if they can.

The female gives birth to either one or two 'live' offspring known as 'Hogs'. As a Hog is not clothed until a year old, the tracker can observe the bold contrast of the beastie's bare torso with the thick fur coat covering the rest of its body. From an early age, the Hogs are taught the importance of preserving and regenerating the woodland environment around them.

Compare and contrast the narrow, long rear pad with that of their domesticated cousins. The lack of claw marks shows how lightly the Hairy Horny Haggis treads over the ground.

TRACKING

EASY ←——————→ HARD

An adult Highland Midge.

The Highland Midge, affectionately known as a 'Midgie', is easy to observe as they actively seek out humans. It grows to a length of 1.2mm, has a wingspan of 1.4mm and is virtually weightless. Although their main food source is nectar, their fearsome reputation is derived from the females' need to engorge blood to help develop their eggs. This tiny beastie has single-handedly ensured that vast tracts of Scotland remain undeveloped by humans to this day.

Highland Midges are very numerous with up to 24 million Larvae per hectare. They thrive on moist soil surrounded by vegetation and have a social hierarchy that is as anarchic as a Bluebottle's.

Interesting Facts

- Only the female Midge drinks blood.
- Collective name - a 'scourge'.
- Breeding season - mainly May to September.
- Potential as a human pet - definitely not!
- A feeding female releases a pheromone into the air telling other females that she has found a good host to suck blood from.

Where found in Scotland

Tracking Tips

A young Highland Midge (Larva).

The female lays eggs in batches of between 30-100 eggs which hatch into live young known as Larvae. Incredibly, by the time the Larva is the age shown above, it will have changed four times (each stage is called an instar). She is now ready to drink a blood meal where she takes about four minutes to drink 0.1 microlitre of blood.

Right: Whilst distinctive, the tiny size of these tracks makes it extremely hard to spot with the human eye.

- Their vast numbers and eagerness to find you, makes this a very easy beastie to track.
- Identification 'call' - high pitched whine of wings in your ear.
- Defensive strategies - none. They are so numerous that no single predator can affect their overall numbers.
- Natural habitat - boggy, acidic areas below 500m in height.
- Behavioural habits - every Midge for itself. They will attack you in large numbers in the hope that some will get the blood meal unswatted!

TRACKING

EASY ⟵⟶ HARD

An adult Hugmahush.

Hugmahush are plentiful but, as they look exactly like real knolls, how can you tell if you have found one? Firstly, look for fresh disturbance marks in the earth around the circumference of the mound. If the tracks are too old and grass has grown over them, then search for rabbit burrows. If there are none, there's a good chance that you have found a Hugmahush as burrows cause draughts and Hugmahush loathe draughts gusting through them. Be prepared for a long wait to confirm your hunch, as once they are settled, Hugmahush can stay put for years!

Hugmahush, being solitary creatures, have no need of social hierarchies as all Hugmahush are deemed equal. They grow to a size similar to that of a hillock whilst gaining their sustenance by absorbing minerals from the earth they are resting upon.

Interesting Facts

- The original land speed record (in the truest sense of the term) was achieved by a Hugmahush travelling between two glens in Sutherland on the 9th of February, 1876.
- Collective name - a 'huggle'.
- Breeding season - Springtime in every Leap Year.
- Potential as a human pet - not very practical unless you want a growing hillock in your lounge!
- The phrase 'Faith will move mountains' is believed to originate from a helpful Hugmahush shepherdess.

Where found in Scotland

A young Hugmahush (Hush).

Hugmahush nest anywhere flat with interesting views. They give birth to one 'live' young known as a 'Hush' who, with the zest of youth, moves his resting place every day without being noticed. Tread carefully or you can easily squash these delicate little creatures. Hush are hard to distinguish from small undulations in the ground though if you use your fingers to press gently upon them, their bodies feel squishy like water-logged earth. Hush take decades to mature into adults. When a Hush has been naughty, its punishment is to remain in one spot i.e. it is said to be 'grounded' (the possible origin of the human term).

Tracking Tips

- Hugmahush have developed the ultimate in camouflage but their size make them relatively easy to track.
- Identification 'call' - an earth tremor often mistaken for an earthquake.
- Defensive strategies - none required.
- Natural habitat - anywhere there is countryside.
- Behavioural habits - deep thinkers who are set in their ways.

A large mud scrape similar to the earth being disturbed by a bulldozer... though without the tank tracks!

TRACKING

EASY ←———————→ HARD

An adult Kelpie.

To all intents and purposes, a Kelpie looks like a horse with two exceptions; large dew claws and razor sharp teeth, both which they try to hide from their potential prey. They lure humans onto their backs for a 'free' ride then dive into the lochan, dragging the unfortunate victim down to its watery lair. It is here that the prey is ripped to pieces and devoured one sliver of flesh at a time.

Kelpies' nests are always accessed by going underwater. These lairs are dry with an air source normally supplied via a hole in the rock ceiling. If human meat is not available, then red deer or sheep will do.

Kelpies are solitary creatures so have no social hierarchy but if they ever do congregate, then it is the strongest stallion that is dominant. The average height of a Kelpie is 160cm to the shoulder and they weigh up to 550 kgs.

Interesting Facts

- Unlike their equine cousins, Kelpies only eat meat so if the horse next to you is 'pretending' to eat grass, beware!
- Collective name - a 'harras'.
- Breeding season - May to July each year.
- Potential as a human pet - definitely not unless you wish to be dinner!
- It is impossible to get off a Kelpie's back until you are in its lair and by then it is too late.

Where found in Scotland

28

Tracking Tips

A young Kelpie (Foal).

A Kelpie gives birth to a 'live' young known as a 'Foal' and the usual size of the litter is one. The Foal is gangly and unsure on its hooves when first born but the lethal dew claw is well developed and a youngster is perfectly capable of ripping a human to shreds if given the chance.

Right: At first glance, it is easy to mistake this for a horse's hoof print until the telltale dew claw mark is noticed at the back of the track.

- Their ability to portray themselves as horses make these a hard (and dangerous) quarry but once a Kelpie's lochan is found, they are easy to observe as they don't hide from humans.
- Identification 'call' - a whinny (indistinguishable from a real horse).
- Defensive strategies - relies on guile to deceive opponents but a formidable adversary when it launches an attack.
- Natural habitat - isolated lochans.
- Behavioural habits - they practise stalking and the art of deception constantly to increase their success rate in hunting for 'fresh meat'.

TRACKING

EASY ←————→ HARD

An adult Loch Ness Monster.

Generally believed to be Plesiosaurs but known locally as Nesses, these leviathans are thought to leave the oceans to raise their young in the safe deep waters of Loch Ness. Throughout this time, the adults must take turns in returning to the sea to feed, as the loch does not contain sufficient fish stocks to sustain a resident population of these creatures. They can grow up to 20 metres in length and weigh in excess of 50 tonnes.

These beasties love to see the excited reactions from passing boats and cars when other Nesses drag logs across the loch's surface, wave their flippers or blow giant air bubbles under the water.

It is believed that the Nesses are probably diurnal but that they choose to come out at night to avoid detection by humans. They have a matriarchal society.

Interesting Facts

- First chronicled encounter with the 'water monster' was by St. Columba in 565 AD.
- Collective name - a 'pod.'
- Breeding season - in the Spring of each Leap Year.
- Potential as a human pet - definitely not!
- They sleep in what look like giant birds' nests secreted in underwater caves at the bottom of Loch Ness.

Where found in Scotland

Tracking Tips

A young Loch Ness Monster (Nester).

Females lay a clutch of up to four eggs every Leap Year. Once hatched, the young are known as 'Nesters' and take years to mature hence the species' slow birth rate. A Nester can swim from birth and is very playful. This natural exuberance can lead to their cover being broken and gives trackers their best chance of observing these beasties in a relaxed atmosphere.

Right: Often mistaken for scuba divers' flippers, these tracks are found around many deep Scottish lochs especially in sandy bays that allow easy access to and from the water.

- A tracker must be prepared for night-time stake outs.
- Identification 'call' - being well-travelled, the Nesses are multi-lingual but their natural call sign is a series of high pitched notes only heard underwater (similar to whale song).
- Defensive strategies - either escape to the open seas or hide in their underwater caves.
- Natural habitat - any big bodies of deep water.
- Behavioural habits - they love travel…and teasing humans!

TRACKING

EASY ←——————→ HARD

MACSPORRAN *Sporranus Mollicate*

An adult MacSporran.

The MacSporrans' red tartan is a warning signal to any foe that they are ferocious fighters who enjoy nothing better than a rough and tumble where someone loses a few teeth (invariably the other creature). They pack a lot of punch for their size being only 60cm tall and weighing around 15kgs. They are obsessed with the sport of caber tossing. Forest clearings are good sites for viewing them during practice sessions. The tracker should always be listening out for the distant sound of axe blows as this may be a MacSporran cutting himself a new caber from the Great Wood of Caledon.

As voracious omnivores, if it is edible, a MacSporran will eat! They live in small villages of traditionally built Scottish Black Houses. They are governed by a chieftain and a council of elders though it is very much a case of 'equals' when dealing on a one to one basis.

Interesting Facts

- MacSporrans never go anywhere without their beloved cabers.
- Collective name - a 'stushie'.
- Breeding season - all year.
- Potential as a human pet - definitely not !
- Humans used to trap these creatures and make sporrans from their pelts.

Where found in Scotland

32

Tracking Tips

A young MacSporran (Poke).

- MacSporran are easy to follow once found. The problem for the tracker is locating one of the few stushies left in the wild.
- Identification 'call' - a growl (similar to that of a Border Terrier).
- Defensive strategies - attack... attack...attack!
- Natural habitat - The Great Wood of Caledon.
- Behavioural habits - hit first and ask questions afterwards!

A MacSporran usually gives birth to just one 'live' young which is known as a 'Poke'. It is so called because of its annoying habit of aggressively and constantly poking you and not stopping until it gets what it wants. Resplendent in tartan nappies, this is one baby that you don't want to make cry. Pokes are encouraged to master pain from an early age, hence the wooden teething caber and the razor sharp axe as a plaything.

The claws project deeply into the mud due to the MacSporran's heavy tread - a sign of the beastie's supreme confidence in a dangerous world.

TRACKING

EASY ⟷ HARD

An adult Moortie.

Interesting Facts

- Moorties love rock music.
- Collective name - a 'cairn'.
- Breeding season - in the winter. The cold helps the females during the birthing process when frost splits the Chukkies away from their bodies (possible origin of the phrase 'A chip off the old block').
- Potential as a human pet - yes, there are occasional human crazes for 'pet rocks'.
- Moorties are classified as neither prey nor predators.

Moorties come in all shapes and sizes but a general rule of thumb is that the older they are, the bigger and heavier they get. They eat any type of fine grit found locally and build their nests in the centre of the rock pile that they herd. Moorties can be solitary or live in groups. Their social hierarchy is very egalitarian with the youngest having the same rights as the oldest.

Visually, it is impossible to tell a Moortie apart from a real rock. A tracker must be prepared for a night-time stake out as this is when Moorties emerge from the midst of their boulders. They become so focused on their rock herding that they forget about hiding from people. This situation changes instantly if Moorties sense human activity in their immediate area.

Where found in Scotland

A young Moortie (Chukkie).

Moorties give birth to litters of four or five offspring known as 'Chukkies'. These youngsters love playing with their building blocks (pebbles) and are often heard whistling as they do so. It is believed that these games help develop their natural herding instincts that will stand them in such good stead in later life. If you ever find small piles of stones next to a boulder field then it is likely that a Moortie family is in residence there.

Right: Note the chiselled square toes and the flat pad of the foot both ideal for giving stability and a low centre of gravity when moving large boulders.

Tracking Tips

- Moorties are masters of blending in with their surroundings.
- Identification 'call' - several 'clicks' like a pebble falling down a scree slope.
- Defensive strategies - they can change colour (chameleon-like) to blend in with any stones that are nearby.
- Natural habitat - anywhere that there are rocks.
- Behavioural habits - their craggy appearance hides a flinty core shown when other animals disturb the Chukkies or their chosen pile of rocks.

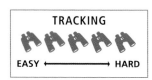

TRACKING

EASY ←——————→ HARD

35

A Silkie

Silkies are often confused with merfolk but they are a completely separate species. As people, Silkies eat the same diet and revel in the different experiences of dry land, doing human activities that are not possible when underwater. When they are in seal form they hunt fish and chase each other through the seaweed forests. Silkies love a good party and enjoy playing practical jokes too. They live in a matriarchal society.

Knowing that you are tracking a Silkie as opposed to an ordinary seal or person can be difficult. It is virtually impossible to distinguish them from seals in the water but small clues are betrayed when they are in human form. Look out for the wearing of seaweed jewellery and the fact that the 'person' never wanders far from the safety of the sea shore. Obviously, if they are bare foot, check between their toes.

Interesting Facts

• A Silkie can make the change from seal to human and vice versa in seconds.

• Collective name - a 'celebration'.

• Breeding season - in the Spring.

• Potential as a human pet - yes. A Silkie can be a companion (never a pet) to a human but if denied access to their skin and a return to the sea, Silkies will die eventually.

• Silkie nests are 'scrapes' in the sand of sheltered beaches on deserted islands.

Where found in Scotland

Tracking Tips

A Silkie Pup

- If you stumble upon a seal skin, then a Silkie will be very close by.
- Identification 'call' - happy singing by the seashore.
- Defensive strategies - flee to the sea.
- Natural habitat - the sea and coastal lands.
- Behavioural habits - Silkies are joyful creatures who relish frolicking in the surf or playing in the sand dunes.

Silkies give birth to one 'live' young per litter. Known as 'Pups', they are very contented offspring. Silkie babies are easily identified in their human form by their distinctive seal pup hair colouring, seaweed nappies and their webbed toes. Being inexperienced, the Pups often discard (as opposed to hide) their seal skins when building sandfish on the beach and sadly, this habit makes them vulnerable to human discovery and exploitation.

Initial impression is that of a human foot print until closer inspection reveals webbed toes.

TRACKING

EASY ⟵⟶ HARD

37

A Witch beside her coracle

They are ruled by a queen, who is the most powerful Witch in her particular Grand Coven.

Interesting Facts

• Many Witches are flying in the more comfortable coracle instead of on the less aerodynamic broomstick these days.

• Collective name - a 'coven'.

• Breeding season - all year round.

• Potential as a human pet - definitely not!

• Skloosh is a gloopy gunge fired from powerful cannon to 'persuade' Faeries to leave a Witch's territory.

Being human, a Witch can look like any other woman which makes recognising them extremely difficult. It is only by noting her daily routine over a period of time, that trackers can be certain that they have identified one. However, if detected, the tracker runs the risk of being turned into a 'standing stone' (the traditional Witch penalty for spying). This punishment accounts for many of these randomly sited stones across Scotland.

As well as 'normal' food, a Witch's diet includes such delicacies as slugs' bogies, spiders' brains and a pinch of bat pooh which may explain why they tend to live alone.

Where found in Scotland

38

A young Witch (Baby)

Witches give birth to 'live' young known as 'Babies' and the size of litter is the same as normal people. They use an old cauldron for the cot as this allows the engrained magic to rub off on the youngster as she sleeps. The first magic that a Baby Witch performs is the 'electric shock' spell using her 'rattle' wand.

Right: A Witch's heel print reveals a cauldron-shaped emblem with two elements to it. The letter 'B' or 'W' signifies whether she is a black or white magic practitioner whilst the figures are her membership number in the relevant Grand Coven.

Tracking Tips

- Be warned! Witches can see into the future (scrying) so they know when you are tracking them before you do.
- Identification 'call' - ranges from an evil cackle to a courteous introduction.
- Defensive strategies - potions, traps, skloosh cannon, 'standing stone' spells … best described as 'offensive defence'.
- Natural habitat - ranges from a grotty hovel to a magnificent castle.
- Behavioural habits - this all depends on whether she practises white or black magic. Generally, white magic is healing and righting wrongs whereas black magic is the opposite.

TRACKING

EASY ←――――――→ HARD

39

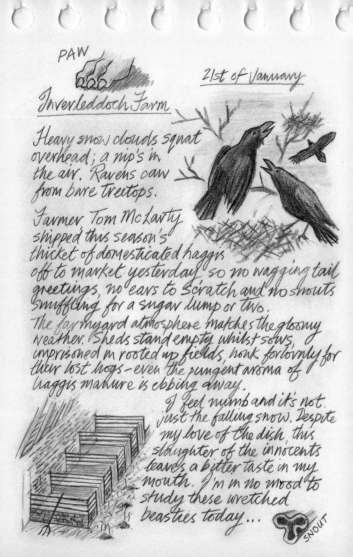

PAW

21st of January

Inverleddoch Farm

Heavy snow clouds squat overhead; a nip's in the air. Ravens caw from bare treetops.

Farmer Tom McLarty shipped this season's thicket of domesticated haggis off to market yesterday, so no wagging tail greetings, no ears to scratch and no snouts snuffling for a sugar lump or two.

The farmyard atmosphere matches the gloomy weather. Sheds stand empty whilst sows, imprisoned in rooted up fields, honk forlornly for their lost hogs – even the pungent aroma of haggis manure is ebbing away.

I feel numb and it's not just the falling snow. Despite my love of the dish, this slaughter of the innocents leaves a bitter taste in my mouth. I'm in no mood to study these wretched beasties today...

SNOUT

9th of February

Scree slopes at base of Corriemor Crags.

In snow hole; sparkling winter sun:
Golden Eagle soaring high overhead.

Moortie gives birth to four
chukkies (paler colour to her
initially). She sat out
overnight squeezing
her flanks and letting the frost split the
youngsters from her sides - she's freezing - me
                                                    too!

I could murder
a mug of hot
chocolate

Panic! A chukkie
fell into a
snow drift -
Mum to the rescue.

Aaargh! My metal monocular
froze to my eyelid!?*!

Lochan an Capall

It's dreich. The tang of damp peat hangs in the air.

Under camouflaged tarpaulin, 500 yards from the Kelpie's lair. Jet black stallion practising dew claw strike moves - fearsome. Luckily, I'm downwind so he hasn't got my scent. Wind had better not change direction!

Note to self
Sphagnum moss comfy... Spiky heather not!

ANIMALS I DON'T WANT TO BE EATEN BY (WONDER WHAT MADE ME THINK OF THIS?)
a) Water Kelpie
b) Praying Mantis
c) Great White Shark
d) Tarantula Spider
e) Crocodile
f) Boa Constrictor

30 MINUTES NOW

I HAVEN'T MOVED A MUSCLE FOR

At least at this altitude there are no midges!

Glen Ogle

5th of May

DRAWN VIA THE MIRROR - JUST IN CASE!

Typical! 'Depressed' rain cloud moping around. When bogle appears drizzle turns to sleety snow. My fruit juice carton freezes into a lollipop →

DREICH AGAIN

On far side of the glen vehicles wind their way up the road oblivious to the danger. I view it all via a plastic mirror (looking directly at a bogle can be fatal).

THE BOGLE IS UNEARTHLY HOWLS GIVE ME THE COLLYWOBBLES

BOGLE TRACKING IS UNPREDICTABLE AND DANGEROUS.

PLASTIC.

AFTER MONOCULAR INCIDENT IN FEBRUARY, I'VE LEARNED THAT COLD METAL AND MY SKIN DON'T MIX

GREAT! THIS ONE'S PLACID AND MY HIDE'S NOT IN ITS FLIGHT PATH. I'M SAFE... 'ISH!?*!

Secluded beach near Applecross

Sun splits a cloudless sky. Gentle sea
breeze carries sounds of laughter and
singing. Silkies, in both human and seal
form frolic and splash in the surf.
A joyous sight. I can't help but smile!

I'VE BEEN PRACTISING
MY DUCK CALLS AND
A SEAGULL HAS
JUST KEECHED
ON MY PAD!
WHY DO PEOPLE
SAY THAT'S LUCKY?
IT STINKS!

SOMEONE IS ENJOYING
THE SEAGULL'S EFFORTS.
IS THERE ANYTHING A FLY
WON'T LAND ON?

I CAN TOUCH MY NOSE WITH MY TONGUE!

SUN'S BLAZING...
I'M ROASTING!

HIGH
MED
LOW
TEMP

BOILING IN
SUMMER!?*!

TWEED-
WARM IN
WINTER

IN ALL MY YEAR'S OF TRACKING,
I'VE NEVER SEEN WHERE A
SILKIE HIDES ITS SEAL SKIN.

SAND GETS EVERY-
WHERE

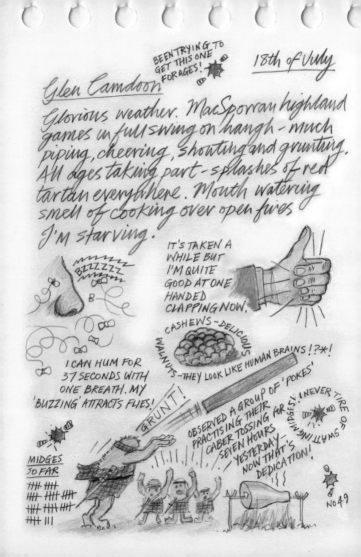

BEEN TRYING TO GET THIS ONE FOR AGES!

18th of July

Glen Camdoon

Glorious weather. MacSporran highland games in full swing on haugh - much piping, cheering, shouting and grunting. All ages taking part - splashes of red tartan everywhere. Mouth watering smell of cooking over open fires I'M starving.

BZZZZZZ

B

IT'S TAKEN A WHILE BUT I'M QUITE GOOD AT ONE HANDED CLAPPING NOW.

CASHEWS - DELICIOUS

WALNUTS - THEY LOOK LIKE HUMAN BRAINS !?✱!

I CAN HUM FOR 37 SECONDS WITH ONE BREATH. MY 'BUZZING' ATTRACTS FLIES!

GRUNT!

OBSERVED A GROUP OF 'POKES' PRACTISING THEIR CABER TOSSING FOR SEVEN HOURS YESTERDAY - NOW THAT'S DEDICATION!

I NEVER TIRE OF SWATTING MIDGES!

MIDGES SO FAR
卌 卌 卌 卌 卌
卌 卌 卌 卌 卌
卌 卌 卌 III

No 49

Urquhart Castle, Loch Ness

Mild; overcast. No hope of a sighting today.
The castle is heaving with tourists in
brightly coloured waterproofs. Monitoring
loch as a constant murmur of numerous
languages washes over me makes for a
pleasant change of circumstance.

ANOTHER DRAW!

POP!

THERE IS A BOY FROM POOLEWE,
WHOSE GUTS ARE A BUBBLING STEW,
GULPING BEANS FOR HIS 'STARTERS',
HE'S KING OF THE FARTERS,
WHEN HE 'POPS', HIS KILT FLIES OFF TOO!

GRRR...

Child skimmed Moortie
into loch. It's taken 40
minutes to 'float' back
to shore. Result?
One furious Moortie!

RANK THE SEASONS (FAVOURITE FIRST):—
SPRING. AUTUMN. SUMMER AND WINTER.

GOLDEN EAGLE SPOTTED IN THE FAR DISTANCE - H3 CAN RELAX!

27th of September

Glen Affric

Lovely late summer's day. In hide since dawn and not a hint of an H3 (Hairy Horny Haggis). Flies and midgies driving me bonkers!?*! The first throaty roars of the annual red deer rut reverberate around the hillsides.

WAIT!!! An H3 emerges warily from hamelldaeme. Eventually it relaxes and plants saplings on edge of forest. It gathers fungi too.

PICKED UP AN OAK LEAF FOR PRESSING INTO MY JOURNAL

I LOVE THE SMELL OF PINE NEEDLES

AAARGH! I NEED THE LOO BUT DON'T WANT TO SCARE H3 AWAY...

Clattie Gagwort's Castle

Halloween. Sea glinting in moonlight.
Castle's highest tower gives me perfect bird's
eye view. Clattie's showing me how she
'dissuades' faeries from trespassing.
It's quiet. Too quiet.

Flash! Coracle's searchlight pinpoints six
terrified faeries caught out in the open.
Seconds later - coracle's cannon roar.
Skloosh! Faeries deluged in smelly viscous
gunge. Yelping, they flee homewards
post-haste!

DASH! THAT SPOTLIGHT GAVE
ME A FRIGHT - I'VE SPILT
MY TEA EVERYWHERE.

CLATTIE WAVES AS SHE AND A FRIEND FLY PAST SILENTLY.
FAERIES BEWARE...

PROBABLY THE LAST MIDGE OF THE YEAR...

I'VE EATEN A WHOLE
BAG OF CARROTS AND
STILL I CAN'T SEE
IN THE DARK.

AH, THIS IS THE LIFE - WARM AND COMFY TRACKING FOR ONCE!

I'M TRAINING MY MIND. CONCENTRATING
UPON NOT THINKING OF BRAMBLE JAM

Glen Strathfarrar

Dull day. Revisiting a potential 'hush' -
it measures 5 paces by 8 paces. Still no
signs of earth disturbance around
circumference or animal burrows. Studied
this all afternoon. Bored! Maybe it IS
just a hillock but something about the
way it 'looks' tells me otherwise...

LIST OF FAVOURITE SWEETIES

a) SOOR PLOOMS
b) HUMBUGS
c) MINT IMPERIALS
d) STRAWBERRY CREMES
e) LIQUORICE STRIPS

NO MIDGES OR FLIES - YA DANCER

OOOPS! PENCIL SLIPPED I'D DOZED OFF!

STOOD ON BOULDER, CLOSED EYES, PRETENDED I WAS
ON A CLIFF EDGE... AND JUMPED. CHEAP THRILL!

BRAMBLE JAM

MADE FUNNY
FACE AS WIND
CHANGED DIRECTION
- FACE DIDN'T STICK!

I REALLY FANCY A PIECE OF TOAST
AND BRAMBLE JAM...